Make the pictures look the same.

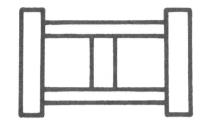 

Draw a ring around the odd one out.

3

Who lives in my house?
Draw the people and pets in your house.

Write the numbers. [ ] people live in my house.

[ ] pets live in my house.

1 2 3 4 5 6 7 8 9 10

Count these things in your house.
Write the number next to the picture.

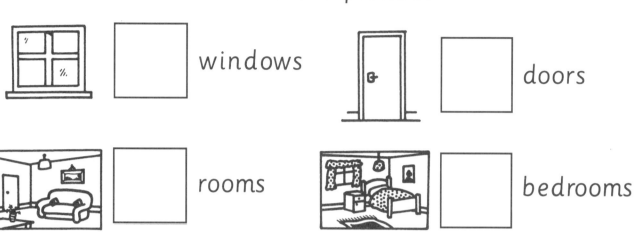

windows

doors

rooms

bedrooms

Use your LEGO to build a house.

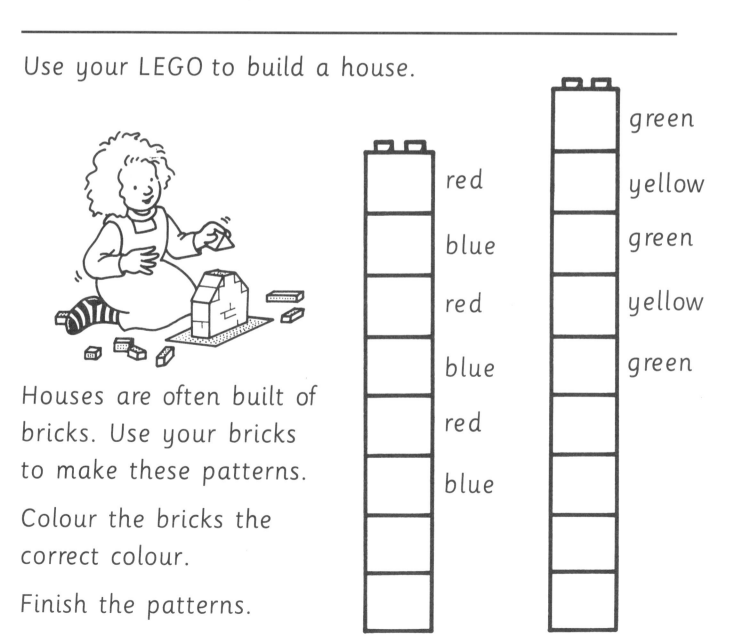

Houses are often built of
bricks. Use your bricks
to make these patterns.

Colour the bricks the
correct colour.

Finish the patterns.

red

blue

red

blue

red

blue

green

yellow

green

yellow

green

My Bedroom

Colour the things that belong together the same colour.

What can you see in the tangle picture?

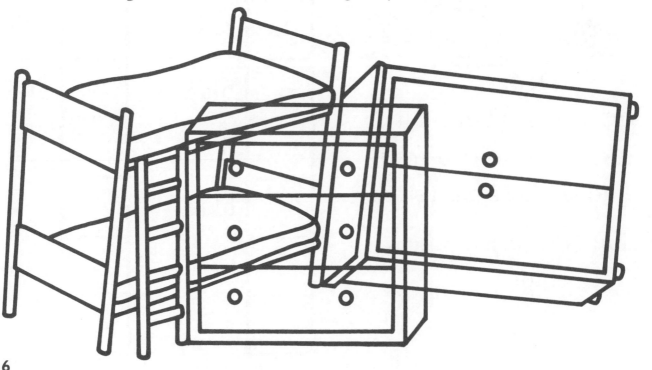

Colour the curtains. Finish the pattern.

What colour are your bedroom curtains?
Colour your curtains here.

Join the dots to finish the picture.

Who is sleeping
in your bed?

The Kitchen

Tidy the kitchen. What can you see?

Some things do not belong in the kitchen.
Colour them green.

Can you match the broken plates?
Join the two pieces to mend the plate.

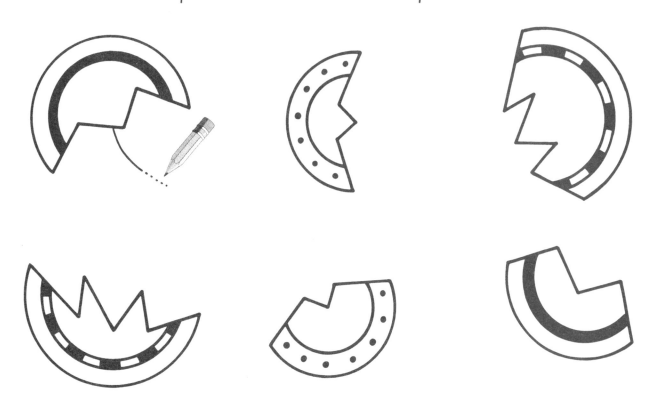

Which is the odd one out? Colour it.

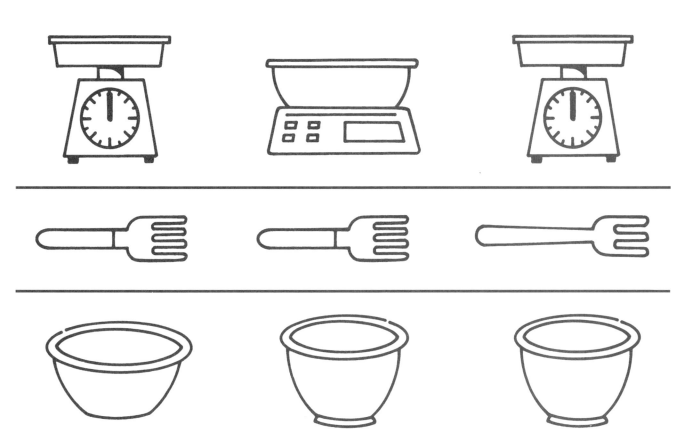

In the Living Room

Mum and Dad are decorating. Tell the story.

Draw a line to join the matching pieces of jigsaw.

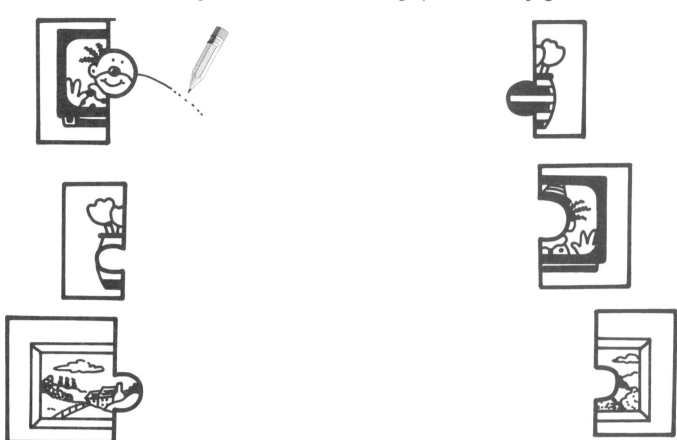

Look at the pictures in each box.
Colour the big one green. Colour the small one yellow.

In the Bathroom

Things I use in the bathroom.
Join the dots to finish the pictures.

Soap

Which takes longer to do?
Put a X on the thing which takes longer to do.

   or

   or

How many? Count and join the pictures to the number.

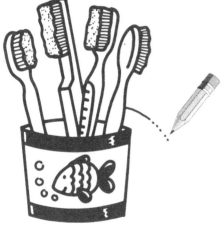

1
2
3
4

The Garage

Take each vehicle into the garage. Trace with a finger, then a pencil.

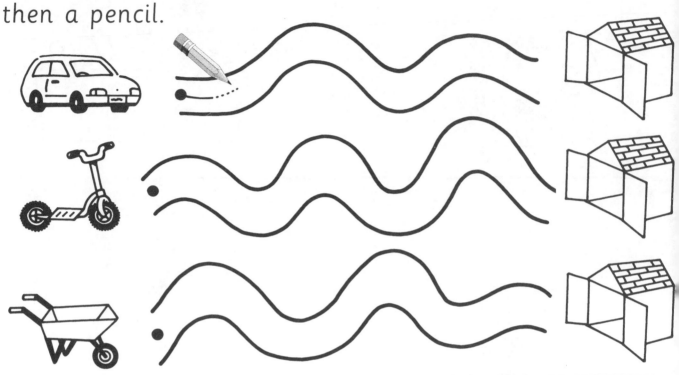

Look on the shelves in the garage. Find these things and colour them.

Count the flower pots.

Look at the pictures in each row.
Circle the group that shows more. Colour it in.

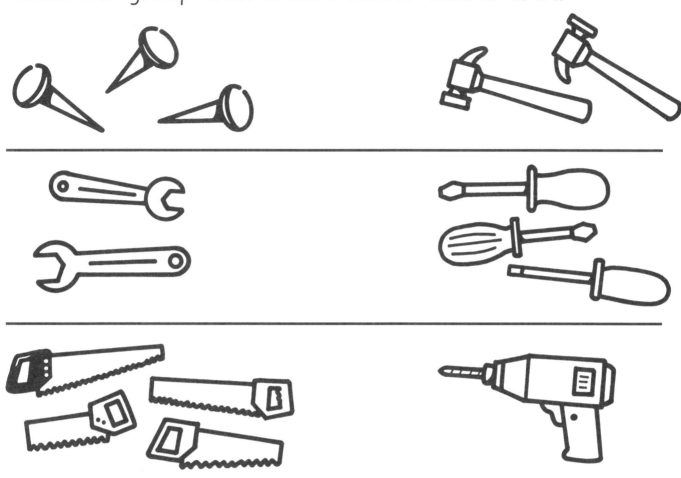

Join the dots to finish the picture.

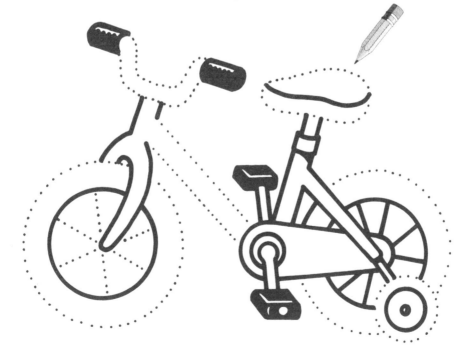

What colour is your bike?

In the Garden

Talk about the picture.

Mum has lost her spade. Can you see it?

How many pets can you see? [ ] pets.

What do you do in the garden?

16

Mum hangs the washing out to dry. Colour the shortest towel red. Colour the longest towel orange.

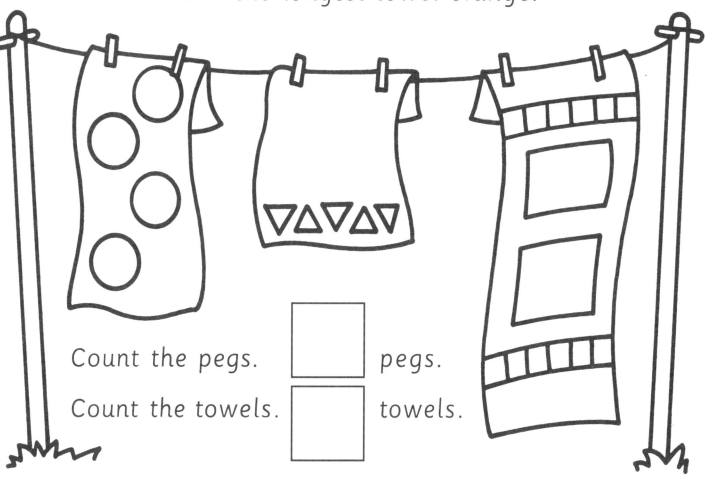

Count the pegs. ☐ pegs.
Count the towels. ☐ towels.

Which hole will each worm pop out of? Use a finger to trace the tunnel first. Then use a pencil or felt tip.

In the Street

Find the hidden numbers.
Colour **1** yellow **2** red **3** blue **4** green **5** purple

Colour the pelican signal the correct colours.

Match to the correct picture.

Do you know the Green Cross Code?

18

Match each person to the correct vehicle.

Look at the small pictures and then find the object in each of the large pictures. Colour it.

NEVER run out from behind an ice cream van.

At the Supermarket

Help Tom choose healthy foods.
Draw a line from healthy foods to the trolley.

Dad and Ellie are looking for soap powder. Show them the way to go. Trace with a finger, then use a pencil.

How many people did they pass? ☐ people.

How many pennies does each item cost?
Put out the correct number of 1p coins for each.
Draw round each 1p coin to show how many.

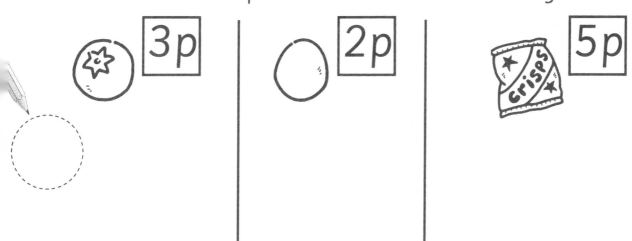

At the Park

Look at the pictures in each box.

Tick ✔ the **shorter** tree.

Tick ✔ the **taller** flower.

Draw a line between the pictures that are opposites.

Look at the picture. What is happening?

Count and write the number in the box.

DO NOT play near water.

Colour the leaves. Continue the pattern.

orange   green   orange   green

red   red   yellow   red   red   yellow

When do leaves change colour?

Schofield & Sims
HELPING CHILDREN TO LEARN

Schofield & Sims was established in 1901 by two headmasters and since then our name has been synonymous with educationally sound texts and teaching materials. Our mission is to publish products which are:

- **Educationally sound • Good value • Written by experienced teachers**
- **• Extensively used in schools, nurseries and play groups**
- **• Used by parents to support their children's learning**

NURSERY ALL ABOUT 2

Series consists of four books; All About Me, All About Where I Live, All About The World I Live In and All About The Weather. Each book is designed to develop young children's awareness of their environment, helping to sharpen their powers of observation and consolidate basic concepts and skills. Enthusiasm for learning is encouraged through fun activities, which give ample opportunity for parental support.

Nursery All About Book 1 - 0 7217 0871 4   **Nursery All About Book 3 -** 0 7217 0873 0

Nursery All About Book 2 - 0 7217 0872 2   **Nursery All About Book 4 -** 0 7217 0874 9

Schofield & Sims pre-school products for 4+ year olds

Posters

Sturdy, laminated posters, full colour, write-on/wipe-off, suitable for wall mounting or desk top use. Over 70 titles including the alphabet, numbers, colours, days, shapes, nursery rhymes, opposites, seasons, time, weather and our bodies.

Information

For further information about products for pre-school, Key Stages 1 and 2, please request our catalogue or visit our website at

www.schofieldandsims.co.uk

Nursery workbooks

Nursery Land

Books 1 - 4

A brand new series of workbooks packed with activities based on popular nursery rhymes, to help develop basic concepts and skills. Includes dot-to-dot, numbers 1-10, colour, shape, size, matching and odd one out.

Nursery Writing

Books 1 - 6

A series of graded workbooks to develop pre-reading and early writing skills, including left-to-right co-ordination, pencil control, visual perception, letter recognition, the alphabet, word recognition, and word writing.

Nursery Activity

Books 1 - 6

An introduction to essential pre-reading and early mathematical skills through a series of graded workbooks. Exercises include left-to-right co-ordination, sequencing, matching, colour, shape and number recognition, counting and number writing practice.

Author   Sally Johnson
Illustrator   Linzi Henry
Cover design   Curve Creative - Bradford

First printed 2000

Reprinted 2003, 2006

Printed by Wyndeham Gait Ltd., Grimsby

Schofield & Sims

Dogley Mill, Fenay Bridge, Huddersfield, HD8 0NQ
Phone 01484 607080   Fax 01484 606815

e-mail sales@schofieldandsims.co.uk

ISBN 0-7217-0872-2

9 780721 708720

Price £1.95
Pre-School
Age Range 4+ years